THIS JOURNAL BELONGS TO:

____

"Maybe the journey isn't so much about becoming anything. Maybe it's about un-becoming everything that isn't really you, so you can be who you were meant to be in the first place."

Paul Coelho

CREATED BY MANIFEST HOUSE

a virtual wellbeing space

www.manifesthouse.com
@manifesthouse

JOURNEY HOME

a guided journal for your journey home to yourself

text "journal" to 602-932-3406
for weekly journal prompts sent right to your phone.

This journal was created just for you, love. Journaling helped me find my way back to myself. It's a way for me to be present in my healing as it's happening. Journaling allows me to see and feel gratitude for all of my messy yet equally beautiful growth. My hope is that this practice of journaling can do the same for you. Consider each entry as a part of your journey; a place to store your most juicy experiences of connecting back to your inner knowing. A place to safekeep your breakthroughs, discoveries, aha moments and divine messages. There's really no wrong way to use this journal, so let your intuition be your guide.

Angelee

founder of
Manifest House

healing event or journal prompt / /

date

I feel:

anxiety joy excitement anger sadness confusion peace hope

circle any combination of emotions

use this space to explore your experience

use this space for insights, aha moments, doodles, or gratitude lists

* these are suggestions, you make the rules

/ /

I feel:

anxiety joy excitement anger sadness confusion peace hope

/ /

now I feel:

/ /

I feel:

anxiety joy excitement anger sadness confusion peace hope

/ /

now I feel:

/ /

I feel:

anxiety joy excitement anger sadness confusion peace hope

/ /

now I feel:

/ /

I feel:

anxiety joy excitement anger sadness confusion peace hope

/ /

now I feel:

/ /

I feel:

anxiety joy excitement anger sadness confusion peace hope

/ /

now I feel:

/ /

I feel:

anxiety joy excitement anger sadness confusion peace hope

/ /

now I feel:

/ /

I feel:

anxiety joy excitement anger sadness confusion peace hope

/ /

now I feel:

I feel:

anxiety joy excitement anger sadness confusion peace hope

/ /

now I feel:

/ /

I feel:

anxiety joy excitement anger sadness confusion peace hope

now I feel:

/ /

I feel:

anxiety joy excitement anger sadness confusion peace hope

/ /

now I feel:

/ /

I feel:

anxiety joy excitement anger sadness confusion peace hope

/ /

now I feel:

/ /

I feel:

anxiety joy excitement anger sadness confusion peace hope

/ /

now I feel:

/ /

I feel:

anxiety joy excitement anger sadness confusion peace hope

/ /

now I feel:

I feel:

anxiety joy excitement anger sadness confusion peace hope

/ /

now I feel:

/ /

I feel:

anxiety joy excitement anger sadness confusion peace hope

/ /

now I feel:

/ /

I feel:

anxiety joy excitement anger sadness confusion peace hope

/ /

now I feel:

/ /

I feel:

anxiety joy excitement anger sadness confusion peace hope

/ /

now I feel:

/ /

I feel:

anxiety joy excitement anger sadness confusion peace hope

/ /

now I feel:

/ /

I feel:

anxiety joy excitement anger sadness confusion peace hope

/ /

now I feel:

/ /

I feel:

anxiety joy excitement anger sadness confusion peace hope

/ /

now I feel:

/ /

I feel:

anxiety joy excitement anger sadness confusion peace hope

/ /

now I feel:

/ /

I feel:

anxiety joy excitement anger sadness confusion peace hope

/ /

now I feel:

/ /

I feel:

anxiety joy excitement anger sadness confusion peace hope

/ /

now I feel:

/ /

I feel:

anxiety joy excitement anger sadness confusion peace hope

/ /

now I feel:

/ /

I feel:

anxiety joy excitement anger sadness confusion peace hope

/ /

now I feel:

/ /

I feel:

anxiety joy excitement anger sadness confusion peace hope

/ /

now I feel:

/ /

I feel:

anxiety joy excitement anger sadness confusion peace hope

now I feel:

/ /

I feel:

anxiety joy excitement anger sadness confusion peace hope

/ /

now I feel:

/ /

I feel:

anxiety joy excitement anger sadness confusion peace hope

/ /

now I feel:

/ /

I feel:

anxiety joy excitement anger sadness confusion peace hope

/ /

now I feel:

Made in the USA
Middletown, DE
07 October 2022

12051306R00071